INTRODUCTION

All expressions of religion, from the Ancient Egyptian cult of sun worship to the Islamic belief in Allah as the one true God, tell us something of the human search for life's meaning and the desire to reach beyond the limits of human experience.

Attempts to understand the world in which we live have led to the posture of the same fundamental questions in every age. Is there a God or Power beyond ourselves? If so, what is the nature of that Power? Why and how was the world created? What are we here for and what happens to us when we die? Religious movements have responded to such questions in a variety of ways, influenced in their search for understanding by the values and structure of the societies in which they have taken root. So as not to appear to use the Christian religion as the axis around which other religions rotate, in this book, the letters BCE meaning 'Before the Common Era' are used instead of BC (Before Christ) and the letters CE meaning the 'Common Era', are used instead of AD (*anno domini*, Latin for 'In the year of Our Lord').

This book introduces children to stories from different religious traditions, ancient and living, that have attempted to make sense of some of the great mysteries of existence. The dramatic lives of the gods of Ancient Greece are contrasted with the haunting presence of the ancestral gods of the Australian Aborigines. Stories from Judaism, Christianity and Islam, the great monotheistic religions of the world, stand in contrast with stories from the Eastern religions of Buddhism and Taoism which strive after an inner state of peace and harmony. Each story, whether from the Iroquois Indians of North America, or from Hinduism's rich treasure trove of scriptures, stands by itself and gives the reader insight into the enchanting and fascinating world of religious belief.

Annabel Shilson-Thomas, 1996

VIKING / PUFFIN

Published by the Penguin Group
Penguin Books Ltd, 27 Wrights Lane, London W8 5TZ, England
Penguin Books USA Inc., 375 Hudson Street, New York, New York 10014, USA
Penguin Books Australia Ltd, Ringwood, Victoria, Australia
Penguin Books Canada Ltd, 10 Alcorn Avenue, Toronto, Ontario, Canada M4V 3B2
Penguin Books (NZ) Ltd, 182–190 Wairau Road, Auckland 10, New Zealand

Penguin Books Ltd, Registered Offices: Harmondsworth, Middlesex, England

First published 1996
1 3 5 7 9 10 8 6 4 2

Text copyright © Annabel Shilson-Thomas, 1996
Illustrations copyright © Barry Smith, 1996

The moral right of the author and illustrator has been asserted

Filmset in Monotype Bembo Schoolbook

Made and printed in Italy by printers srl – Trento

A CIP catalogue record for this book is available from the British Library

ISBN 0–670–85895–1 Hardback
ISBN 0–140–55477–7 Paperback

A FIRST PUFFIN
PICTURE BOOK OF
Stories from
World Religions

Annabel Shilson-Thomas
Illustrated by Barry Smith

For Hugh

VIKING
PUFFIN

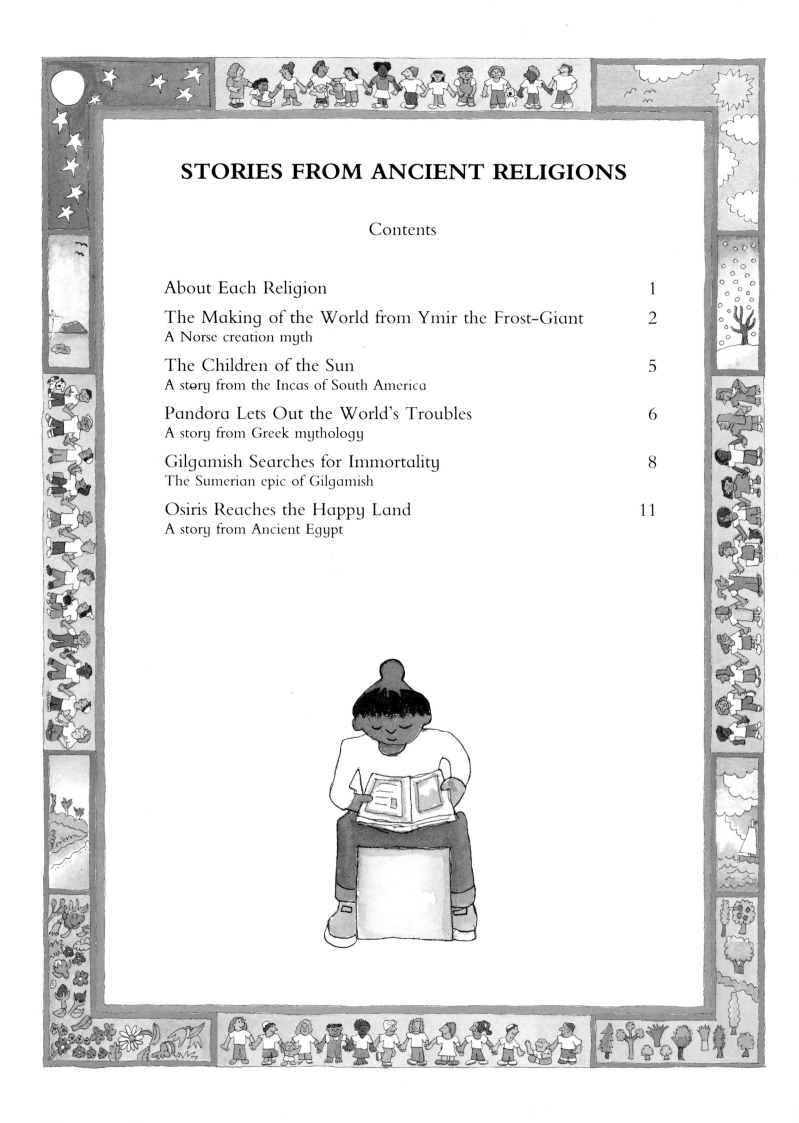

STORIES FROM ANCIENT RELIGIONS

Contents

About Each Religion 1

The Making of the World from Ymir the Frost-Giant 2
A Norse creation myth

The Children of the Sun 5
A story from the Incas of South America

Pandora Lets Out the World's Troubles 6
A story from Greek mythology

Gilgamish Searches for Immortality 8
The Sumerian epic of Gilgamish

Osiris Reaches the Happy Land 11
A story from Ancient Egypt

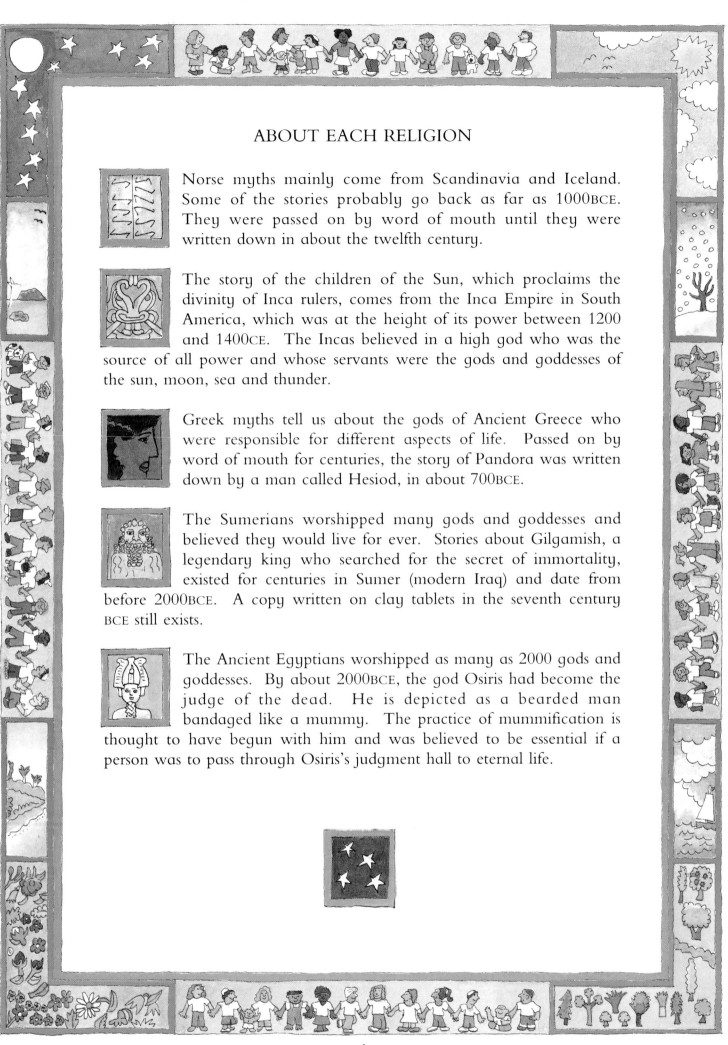

ABOUT EACH RELIGION

Norse myths mainly come from Scandinavia and Iceland. Some of the stories probably go back as far as 1000BCE. They were passed on by word of mouth until they were written down in about the twelfth century.

The story of the children of the Sun, which proclaims the divinity of Inca rulers, comes from the Inca Empire in South America, which was at the height of its power between 1200 and 1400CE. The Incas believed in a high god who was the source of all power and whose servants were the gods and goddesses of the sun, moon, sea and thunder.

Greek myths tell us about the gods of Ancient Greece who were responsible for different aspects of life. Passed on by word of mouth for centuries, the story of Pandora was written down by a man called Hesiod, in about 700BCE.

The Sumerians worshipped many gods and goddesses and believed they would live for ever. Stories about Gilgamish, a legendary king who searched for the secret of immortality, existed for centuries in Sumer (modern Iraq) and date from before 2000BCE. A copy written on clay tablets in the seventh century BCE still exists.

The Ancient Egyptians worshipped as many as 2000 gods and goddesses. By about 2000BCE, the god Osiris had become the judge of the dead. He is depicted as a bearded man bandaged like a mummy. The practice of mummification is thought to have begun with him and was believed to be essential if a person was to pass through Osiris's judgment hall to eternal life.

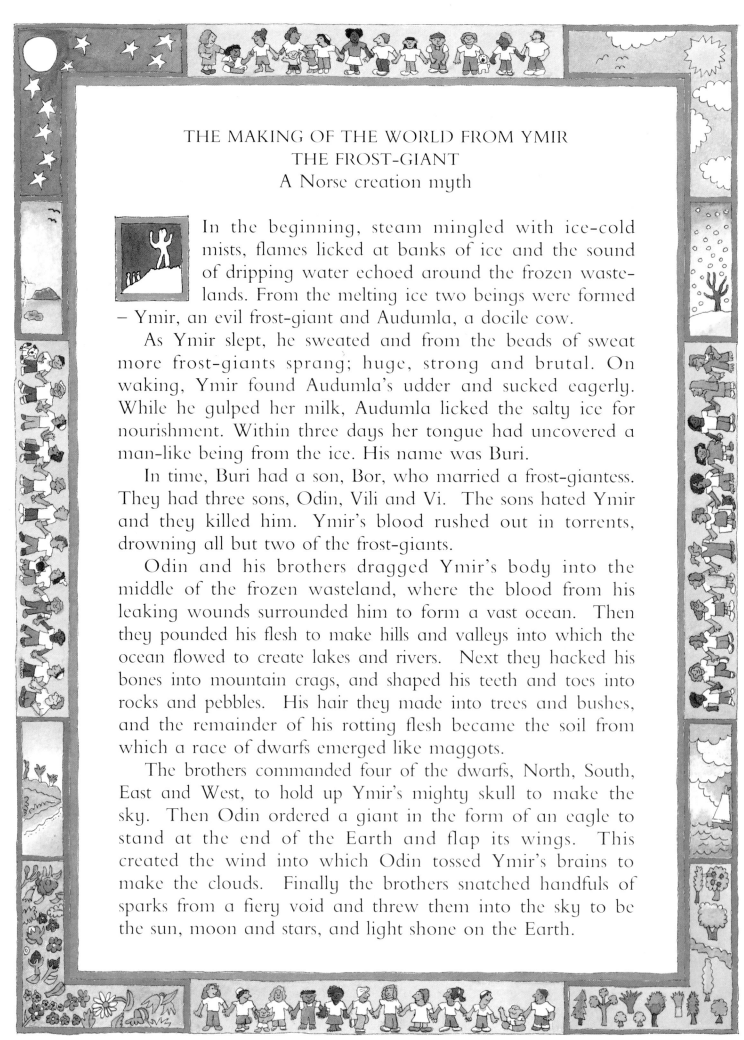

THE MAKING OF THE WORLD FROM YMIR
THE FROST-GIANT
A Norse creation myth

In the beginning, steam mingled with ice-cold mists, flames licked at banks of ice and the sound of dripping water echoed around the frozen wastelands. From the melting ice two beings were formed – Ymir, an evil frost-giant and Audumla, a docile cow.

As Ymir slept, he sweated and from the beads of sweat more frost-giants sprang; huge, strong and brutal. On waking, Ymir found Audumla's udder and sucked eagerly. While he gulped her milk, Audumla licked the salty ice for nourishment. Within three days her tongue had uncovered a man-like being from the ice. His name was Buri.

In time, Buri had a son, Bor, who married a frost-giantess. They had three sons, Odin, Vili and Vi. The sons hated Ymir and they killed him. Ymir's blood rushed out in torrents, drowning all but two of the frost-giants.

Odin and his brothers dragged Ymir's body into the middle of the frozen wasteland, where the blood from his leaking wounds surrounded him to form a vast ocean. Then they pounded his flesh to make hills and valleys into which the ocean flowed to create lakes and rivers. Next they hacked his bones into mountain crags, and shaped his teeth and toes into rocks and pebbles. His hair they made into trees and bushes, and the remainder of his rotting flesh became the soil from which a race of dwarfs emerged like maggots.

The brothers commanded four of the dwarfs, North, South, East and West, to hold up Ymir's mighty skull to make the sky. Then Odin ordered a giant in the form of an eagle to stand at the end of the Earth and flap its wings. This created the wind into which Odin tossed Ymir's brains to make the clouds. Finally the brothers snatched handfuls of sparks from a fiery void and threw them into the sky to be the sun, moon and stars, and light shone on the Earth.

4

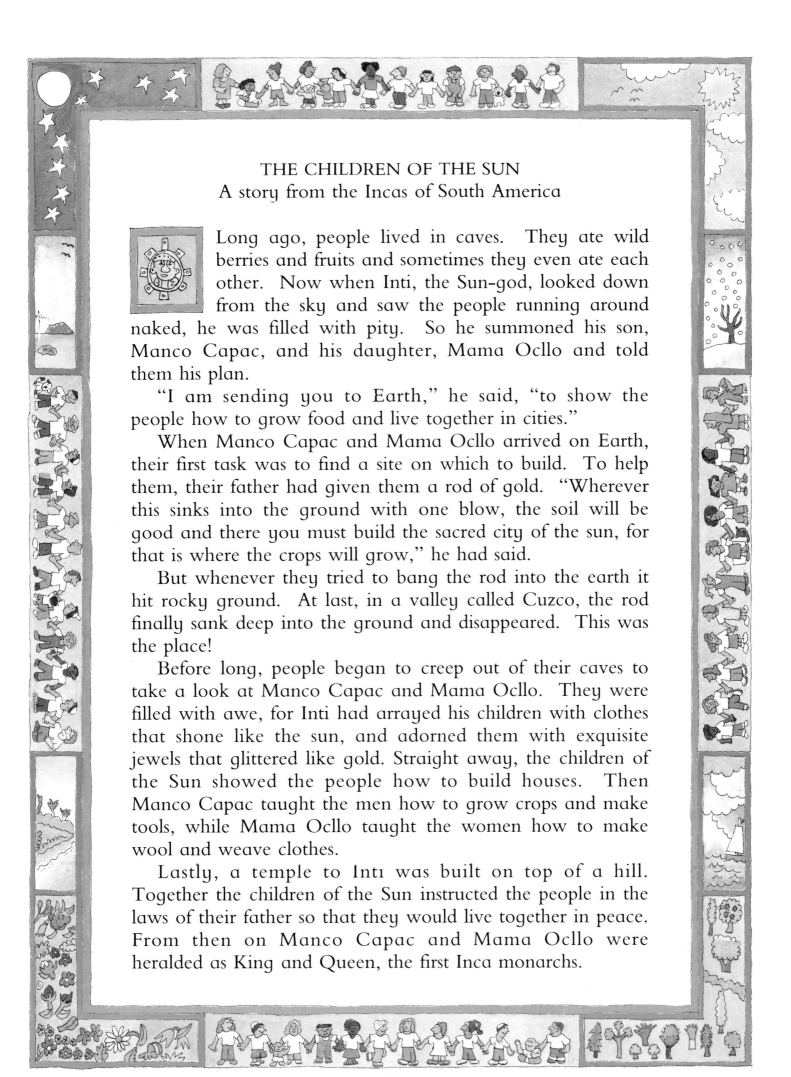

THE CHILDREN OF THE SUN
A story from the Incas of South America

Long ago, people lived in caves. They ate wild berries and fruits and sometimes they even ate each other. Now when Inti, the Sun-god, looked down from the sky and saw the people running around naked, he was filled with pity. So he summoned his son, Manco Capac, and his daughter, Mama Ocllo and told them his plan.

"I am sending you to Earth," he said, "to show the people how to grow food and live together in cities."

When Manco Capac and Mama Ocllo arrived on Earth, their first task was to find a site on which to build. To help them, their father had given them a rod of gold. "Wherever this sinks into the ground with one blow, the soil will be good and there you must build the sacred city of the sun, for that is where the crops will grow," he had said.

But whenever they tried to bang the rod into the earth it hit rocky ground. At last, in a valley called Cuzco, the rod finally sank deep into the ground and disappeared. This was the place!

Before long, people began to creep out of their caves to take a look at Manco Capac and Mama Ocllo. They were filled with awe, for Inti had arrayed his children with clothes that shone like the sun, and adorned them with exquisite jewels that glittered like gold. Straight away, the children of the Sun showed the people how to build houses. Then Manco Capac taught the men how to grow crops and make tools, while Mama Ocllo taught the women how to make wool and weave clothes.

Lastly, a temple to Inti was built on top of a hill. Together the children of the Sun instructed the people in the laws of their father so that they would live together in peace. From then on Manco Capac and Mama Ocllo were heralded as King and Queen, the first Inca monarchs.

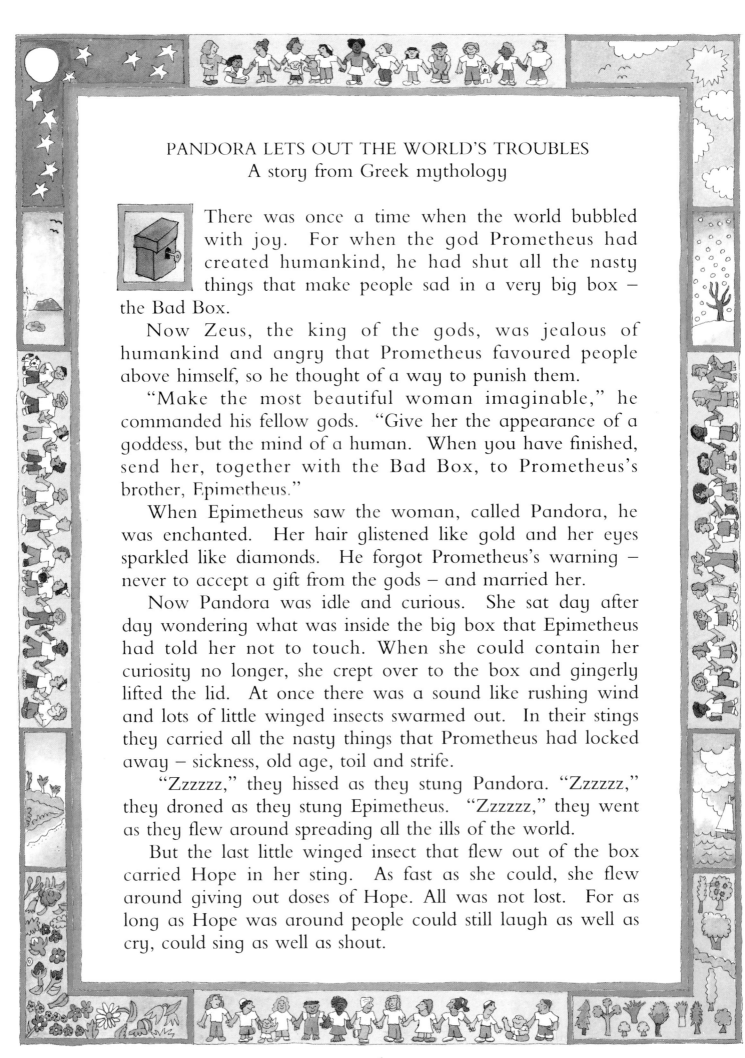

PANDORA LETS OUT THE WORLD'S TROUBLES
A story from Greek mythology

There was once a time when the world bubbled with joy. For when the god Prometheus had created humankind, he had shut all the nasty things that make people sad in a very big box – the Bad Box.

Now Zeus, the king of the gods, was jealous of humankind and angry that Prometheus favoured people above himself, so he thought of a way to punish them.

"Make the most beautiful woman imaginable," he commanded his fellow gods. "Give her the appearance of a goddess, but the mind of a human. When you have finished, send her, together with the Bad Box, to Prometheus's brother, Epimetheus."

When Epimetheus saw the woman, called Pandora, he was enchanted. Her hair glistened like gold and her eyes sparkled like diamonds. He forgot Prometheus's warning – never to accept a gift from the gods – and married her.

Now Pandora was idle and curious. She sat day after day wondering what was inside the big box that Epimetheus had told her not to touch. When she could contain her curiosity no longer, she crept over to the box and gingerly lifted the lid. At once there was a sound like rushing wind and lots of little winged insects swarmed out. In their stings they carried all the nasty things that Prometheus had locked away – sickness, old age, toil and strife.

"Zzzzzz," they hissed as they stung Pandora. "Zzzzzz," they droned as they stung Epimetheus. "Zzzzzz," they went as they flew around spreading all the ills of the world.

But the last little winged insect that flew out of the box carried Hope in her sting. As fast as she could, she flew around giving out doses of Hope. All was not lost. For as long as Hope was around people could still laugh as well as cry, could sing as well as shout.

6

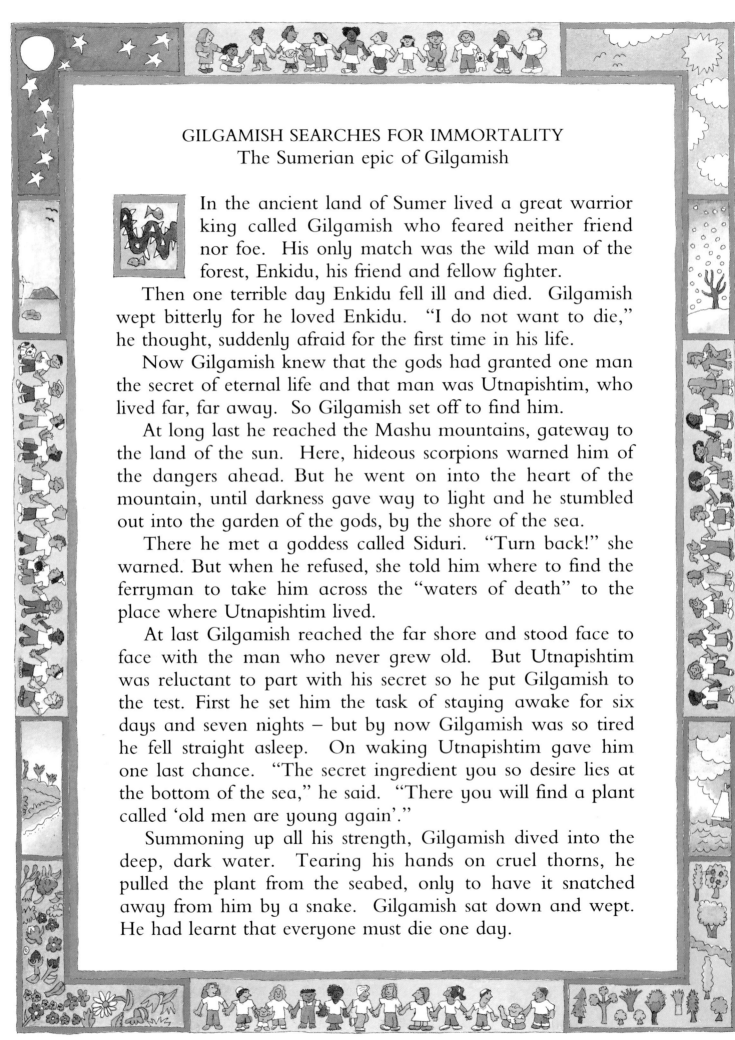

GILGAMISH SEARCHES FOR IMMORTALITY
The Sumerian epic of Gilgamish

In the ancient land of Sumer lived a great warrior king called Gilgamish who feared neither friend nor foe. His only match was the wild man of the forest, Enkidu, his friend and fellow fighter.

Then one terrible day Enkidu fell ill and died. Gilgamish wept bitterly for he loved Enkidu. "I do not want to die," he thought, suddenly afraid for the first time in his life.

Now Gilgamish knew that the gods had granted one man the secret of eternal life and that man was Utnapishtim, who lived far, far away. So Gilgamish set off to find him.

At long last he reached the Mashu mountains, gateway to the land of the sun. Here, hideous scorpions warned him of the dangers ahead. But he went on into the heart of the mountain, until darkness gave way to light and he stumbled out into the garden of the gods, by the shore of the sea.

There he met a goddess called Siduri. "Turn back!" she warned. But when he refused, she told him where to find the ferryman to take him across the "waters of death" to the place where Utnapishtim lived.

At last Gilgamish reached the far shore and stood face to face with the man who never grew old. But Utnapishtim was reluctant to part with his secret so he put Gilgamish to the test. First he set him the task of staying awake for six days and seven nights – but by now Gilgamish was so tired he fell straight asleep. On waking Utnapishtim gave him one last chance. "The secret ingredient you so desire lies at the bottom of the sea," he said. "There you will find a plant called 'old men are young again'."

Summoning up all his strength, Gilgamish dived into the deep, dark water. Tearing his hands on cruel thorns, he pulled the plant from the seabed, only to have it snatched away from him by a snake. Gilgamish sat down and wept. He had learnt that everyone must die one day.

OSIRIS REACHES THE HAPPY LAND
A story from Ancient Egypt

A long, long time ago, a special king was born in Egypt. His mother was the goddess of Heaven and his father the god of Earth. The king's name was Osiris and he was very wise. He taught his people how to live and work together, as well as how to understand the teachings of the gods.

Now Osiris married his sister, Isis, and they were very happy. This made their brother, Set, jealous – it seemed as if Osiris had everything. So Set thought of a plot to get rid of his brother. He ordered a beautiful wooden chest to be made to the king's measurements and promised it to whomever fitted inside most exactly. When Osiris tried it for size, Set's men immediately bolted the lid. Then they hurried away with the chest and threw it into the river Nile.

Meanwhile, Isis was kept prisoner by Set – but she was determined to escape and find her husband's body. Isis tricked her captors and ran away in search of the chest. After many years of searching, she discovered it resting in the trunk of a tree, far away from home. Lovingly, she journeyed back with it to Egypt.

Set was seized with rage. He hunted down the chest and chopped Osiris's body into fourteen pieces, which he flung in every direction. But, fragment by fragment, Isis found and pieced together her husband's body. Carefully, she enclosed it in wax and bound it in linen cloths to make the first mummy. Then using the magic teachings of Osiris, she summoned him back to life.

Osiris rose to live for ever in a peaceful land beyond the sky. Here he judged the souls of the dead by weighing their hearts against a feather, called the Feather of Truth. Those who hearts were heavy with bad deeds were fed to a hungry monster. But those whose hearts were as light as the feather were granted a new life in Osiris's happy kingdom.

STORIES FROM THE WORLD'S OLDEST LIVING RELIGIOUS TRADITIONS

Contents

About Each Religion   13

The Cosmic Battle   14
A Creation story from the Maoris of New Zealand

Meeka the Moon Loses his Fire   16
A story from the Aborigines of Australia

How the Earth was Made   19
A story from the Iroquois people of North America

God Escapes to the Sky   20
A story from the Barotse people of Zambia

ABOUT EACH RELIGION

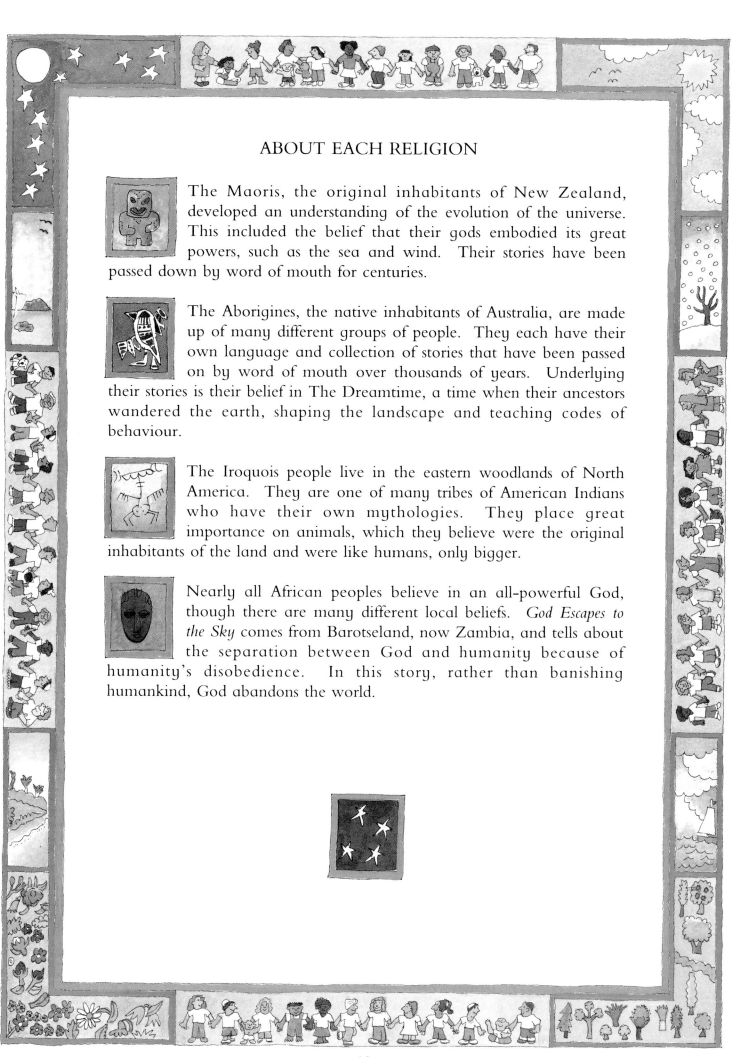

The Maoris, the original inhabitants of New Zealand, developed an understanding of the evolution of the universe. This included the belief that their gods embodied its great powers, such as the sea and wind. Their stories have been passed down by word of mouth for centuries.

The Aborigines, the native inhabitants of Australia, are made up of many different groups of people. They each have their own language and collection of stories that have been passed on by word of mouth over thousands of years. Underlying their stories is their belief in The Dreamtime, a time when their ancestors wandered the earth, shaping the landscape and teaching codes of behaviour.

The Iroquois people live in the eastern woodlands of North America. They are one of many tribes of American Indians who have their own mythologies. They place great importance on animals, which they believe were the original inhabitants of the land and were like humans, only bigger.

Nearly all African peoples believe in an all-powerful God, though there are many different local beliefs. *God Escapes to the Sky* comes from Barotseland, now Zambia, and tells about the separation between God and humanity because of humanity's disobedience. In this story, rather than banishing humankind, God abandons the world.

THE COSMIC BATTLE
A Creation story from the Maoris of New Zealand

In the beginning, Sky Father and Earth Mother clung together in the darkness. Squashed between them lay their children, the gods Wind, Forest, Sea, Food and Fierce Man. At last Fierce Man could stand it no longer.

"Let us kill our parents so we can be free," he raged. Gentle Forest thought it would be better to separate them. All but Wind agreed. He wanted things to stay the same.

Wind sulked as his brothers struggled to prise Sky Father and Earth Mother apart. Forest planted his head on his mother and his feet on his father and then heaved and pushed. All of a sudden, Sky Father let out a mighty roar. Off into space he hurled and from the folds of Earth Mother's body a multitude of human beings crawled out into the light.

At once Forest clothed Earth Mother with green grass and trees, a home for all living things. But Wind wanted revenge. So he blew with all his might, knocking the trees to the ground. Then he turned on Sea, sending the fish deep into the water, and the reptiles scuttling into the forest. This made Sea very angry, for he believed the reptiles belonged to him and not to Forest. So he made his waves as high as possible, sinking the fishing boats made from Forest's trees and drowning Fierce Man's children.

Meanwhile Food had hidden underground, well away from the anger of Wind, so Wind turned his attention to Fierce Man. But however much he huffed and he puffed, Fierce Man stood firm.

Now Fierce Man wanted to be the leader of his brothers, so he ate animals from the forest, fish from the sea and vegetables from the ground. But there was one thing he could not eat and that was the wind. So Wind remained his enemy, raging against humankind both on land and at sea.

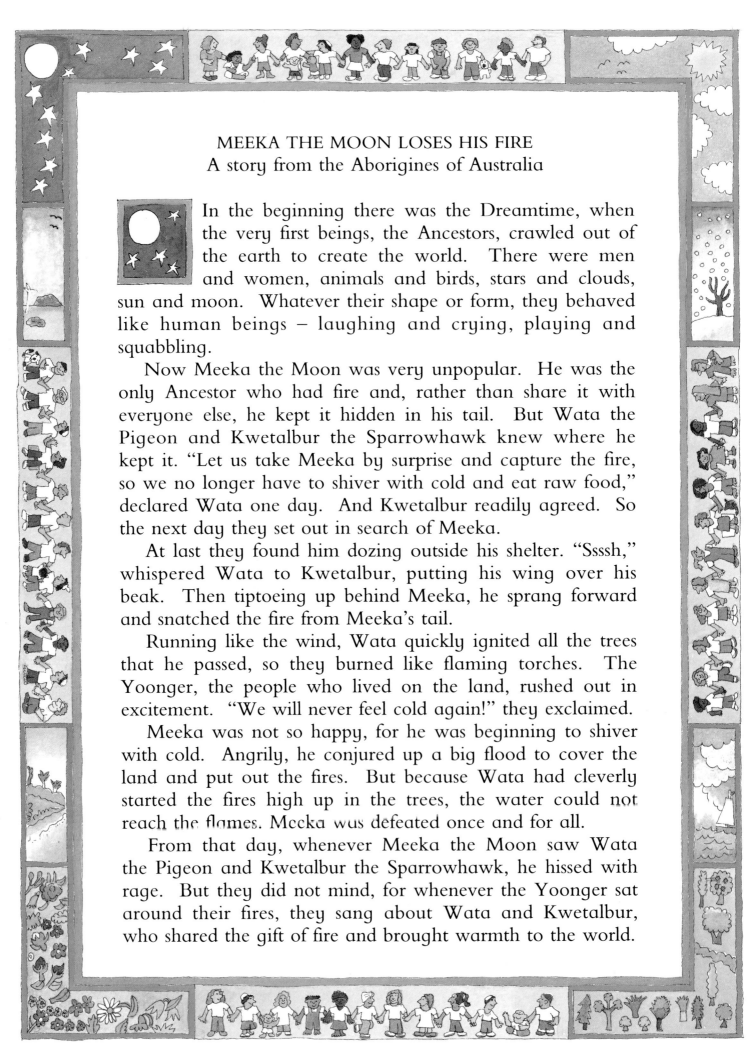

MEEKA THE MOON LOSES HIS FIRE
A story from the Aborigines of Australia

In the beginning there was the Dreamtime, when the very first beings, the Ancestors, crawled out of the earth to create the world. There were men and women, animals and birds, stars and clouds, sun and moon. Whatever their shape or form, they behaved like human beings – laughing and crying, playing and squabbling.

Now Meeka the Moon was very unpopular. He was the only Ancestor who had fire and, rather than share it with everyone else, he kept it hidden in his tail. But Wata the Pigeon and Kwetalbur the Sparrowhawk knew where he kept it. "Let us take Meeka by surprise and capture the fire, so we no longer have to shiver with cold and eat raw food," declared Wata one day. And Kwetalbur readily agreed. So the next day they set out in search of Meeka.

At last they found him dozing outside his shelter. "Ssssh," whispered Wata to Kwetalbur, putting his wing over his beak. Then tiptoeing up behind Meeka, he sprang forward and snatched the fire from Meeka's tail.

Running like the wind, Wata quickly ignited all the trees that he passed, so they burned like flaming torches. The Yoonger, the people who lived on the land, rushed out in excitement. "We will never feel cold again!" they exclaimed.

Meeka was not so happy, for he was beginning to shiver with cold. Angrily, he conjured up a big flood to cover the land and put out the fires. But because Wata had cleverly started the fires high up in the trees, the water could not reach the flames. Meeka was defeated once and for all.

From that day, whenever Meeka the Moon saw Wata the Pigeon and Kwetalbur the Sparrowhawk, he hissed with rage. But they did not mind, for whenever the Yoonger sat around their fires, they sang about Wata and Kwetalbur, who shared the gift of fire and brought warmth to the world.

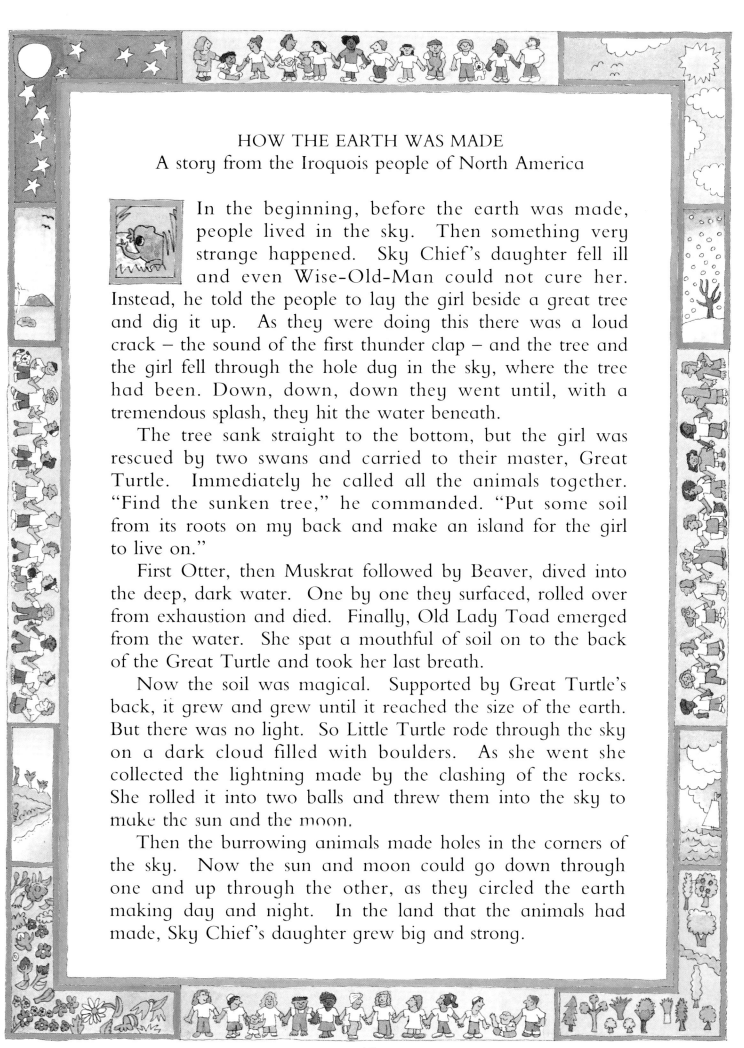

HOW THE EARTH WAS MADE
A story from the Iroquois people of North America

In the beginning, before the earth was made, people lived in the sky. Then something very strange happened. Sky Chief's daughter fell ill and even Wise-Old-Man could not cure her. Instead, he told the people to lay the girl beside a great tree and dig it up. As they were doing this there was a loud crack – the sound of the first thunder clap – and the tree and the girl fell through the hole dug in the sky, where the tree had been. Down, down, down they went until, with a tremendous splash, they hit the water beneath.

The tree sank straight to the bottom, but the girl was rescued by two swans and carried to their master, Great Turtle. Immediately he called all the animals together. "Find the sunken tree," he commanded. "Put some soil from its roots on my back and make an island for the girl to live on."

First Otter, then Muskrat followed by Beaver, dived into the deep, dark water. One by one they surfaced, rolled over from exhaustion and died. Finally, Old Lady Toad emerged from the water. She spat a mouthful of soil on to the back of the Great Turtle and took her last breath.

Now the soil was magical. Supported by Great Turtle's back, it grew and grew until it reached the size of the earth. But there was no light. So Little Turtle rode through the sky on a dark cloud filled with boulders. As she went she collected the lightning made by the clashing of the rocks. She rolled it into two balls and threw them into the sky to make the sun and the moon.

Then the burrowing animals made holes in the corners of the sky. Now the sun and moon could go down through one and up through the other, as they circled the earth making day and night. In the land that the animals had made, Sky Chief's daughter grew big and strong.

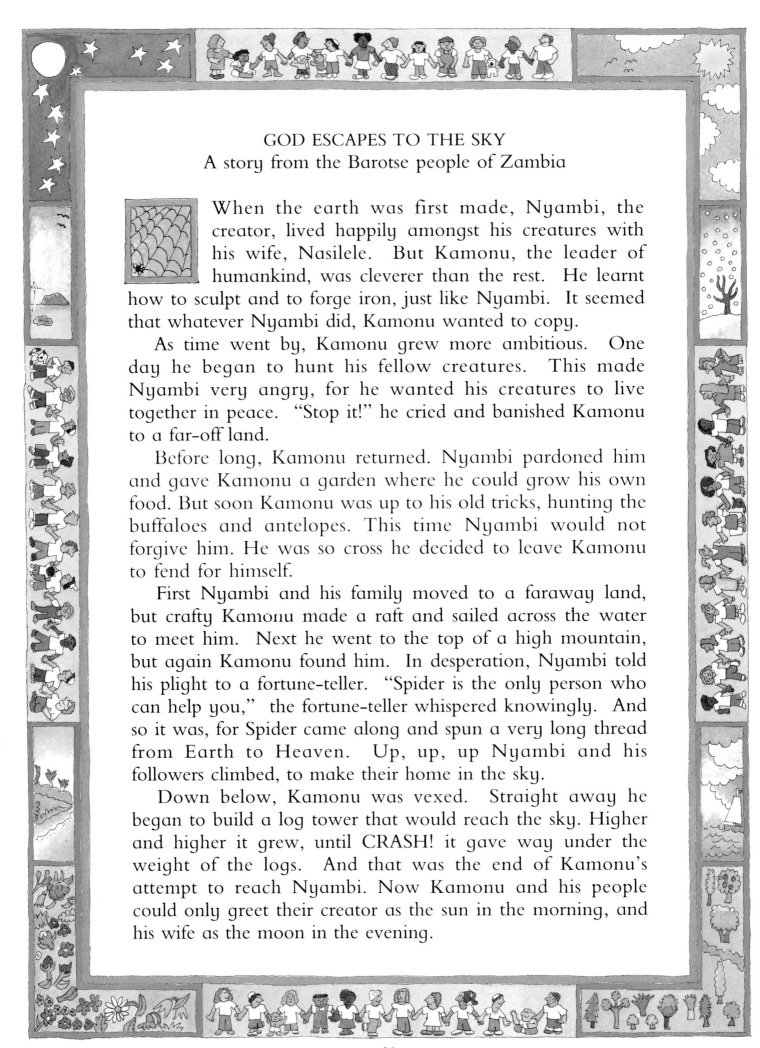

GOD ESCAPES TO THE SKY
A story from the Barotse people of Zambia

When the earth was first made, Nyambi, the creator, lived happily amongst his creatures with his wife, Nasilele. But Kamonu, the leader of humankind, was cleverer than the rest. He learnt how to sculpt and to forge iron, just like Nyambi. It seemed that whatever Nyambi did, Kamonu wanted to copy.

As time went by, Kamonu grew more ambitious. One day he began to hunt his fellow creatures. This made Nyambi very angry, for he wanted his creatures to live together in peace. "Stop it!" he cried and banished Kamonu to a far-off land.

Before long, Kamonu returned. Nyambi pardoned him and gave Kamonu a garden where he could grow his own food. But soon Kamonu was up to his old tricks, hunting the buffaloes and antelopes. This time Nyambi would not forgive him. He was so cross he decided to leave Kamonu to fend for himself.

First Nyambi and his family moved to a faraway land, but crafty Kamonu made a raft and sailed across the water to meet him. Next he went to the top of a high mountain, but again Kamonu found him. In desperation, Nyambi told his plight to a fortune-teller. "Spider is the only person who can help you," the fortune-teller whispered knowingly. And so it was, for Spider came along and spun a very long thread from Earth to Heaven. Up, up, up Nyambi and his followers climbed, to make their home in the sky.

Down below, Kamonu was vexed. Straight away he began to build a log tower that would reach the sky. Higher and higher it grew, until CRASH! it gave way under the weight of the logs. And that was the end of Kamonu's attempt to reach Nyambi. Now Kamonu and his people could only greet their creator as the sun in the morning, and his wife as the moon in the evening.

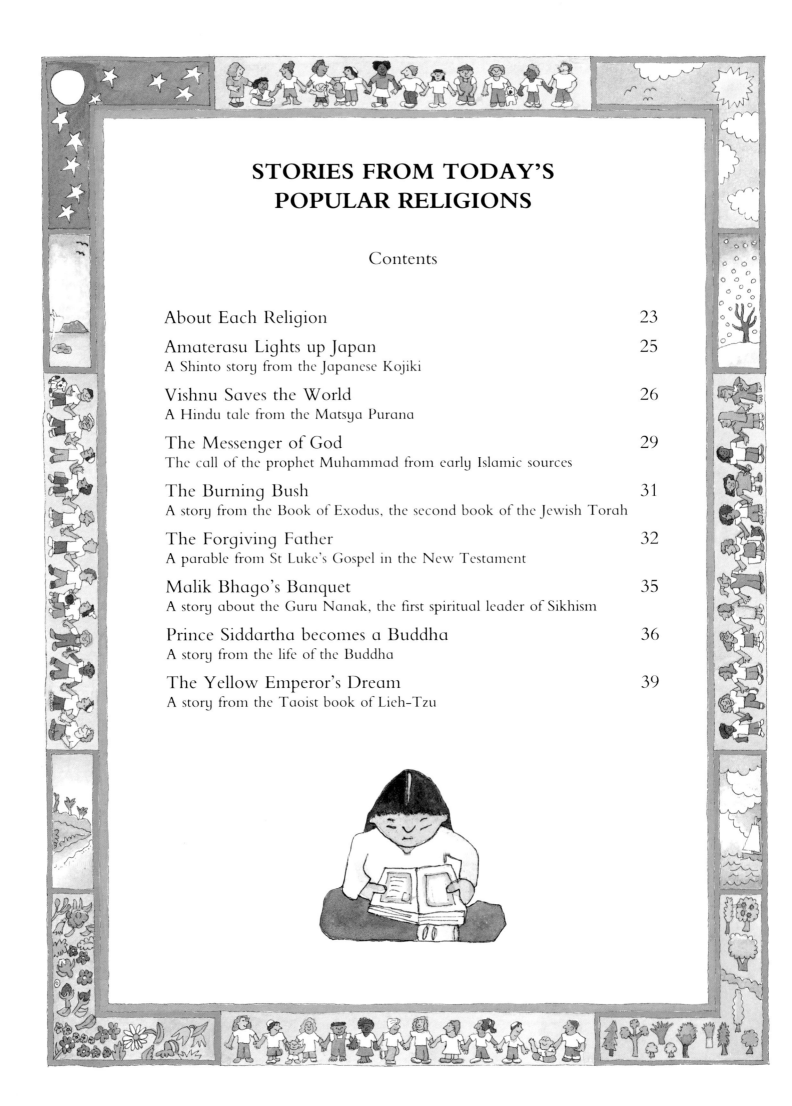

STORIES FROM TODAY'S POPULAR RELIGIONS

Contents

About Each Religion   23

Amaterasu Lights up Japan   25
A Shinto story from the Japanese Kojiki

Vishnu Saves the World   26
A Hindu tale from the Matsya Purana

The Messenger of God   29
The call of the prophet Muhammad from early Islamic sources

The Burning Bush   31
A story from the Book of Exodus, the second book of the Jewish Torah

The Forgiving Father   32
A parable from St Luke's Gospel in the New Testament

Malik Bhago's Banquet   35
A story about the Guru Nanak, the first spiritual leader of Sikhism

Prince Siddartha becomes a Buddha   36
A story from the life of the Buddha

The Yellow Emperor's Dream   39
A story from the Taoist book of Lieh-Tzu

ABOUT EACH RELIGION

Shinto is the national religion of Japan. Its myths and legends tell of the creation of Japan and its people by Kami (gods). Its two major sacred texts, the Kojiki and the Nihongi, were compiled in the eighth century CE.

Hinduism, the world's oldest living religion, developed in India. Hindus worship many gods, believed to be different manifestations of "brahman", the ultimate power. Hinduism has several sacred texts, including the Matsya Purana.

Islam took root in Arabia around 1400 years ago. Its followers (Muslims) believe that their holy book, the Qu'ran, is the culmination of the revelations given to Jews and Christians, and contains every word given by Allah (God) to the prophet Muhammad.

The history of the Jews, as told in the Tenach, goes back over 4000 years, when God made a covenant (contract) with their ancestor, Abraham. This covenant was later extended after their forebears escaped from slavery in Egypt and became God's chosen people.

Christianity began in Palestine about 2000 years ago, when Jesus, a Jewish teacher and healer, was crucified. His followers claim that he rose from the dead and is the Christ, the Son of God. The Christian holy book is The Bible.

Sikhism was founded over five hundred years ago by Guru Nanak, a man who believed in the equality of all people before God. After his death, Sikh beliefs were passed down through a chain of gurus (teachers), until their scriptures, the Guru Granth Sahib, became their guide.

Buddhism began in India, around 500BCE, with a man called Siddhartha Guatama, who sought to understand the nature of suffering. His wisdom earned him the title "enlightened one" and his teachings spread to other eastern countries.

Taoism is more a Chinese philosphy (knowledge obtained by human reason) than a religion. The Tao is the path along which the natural world moves, but humankind is unsure which way to go, so has to search for the Tao.

24

AMATERASU LIGHTS UP JAPAN
A Shinto story from the Japanese Kojiki

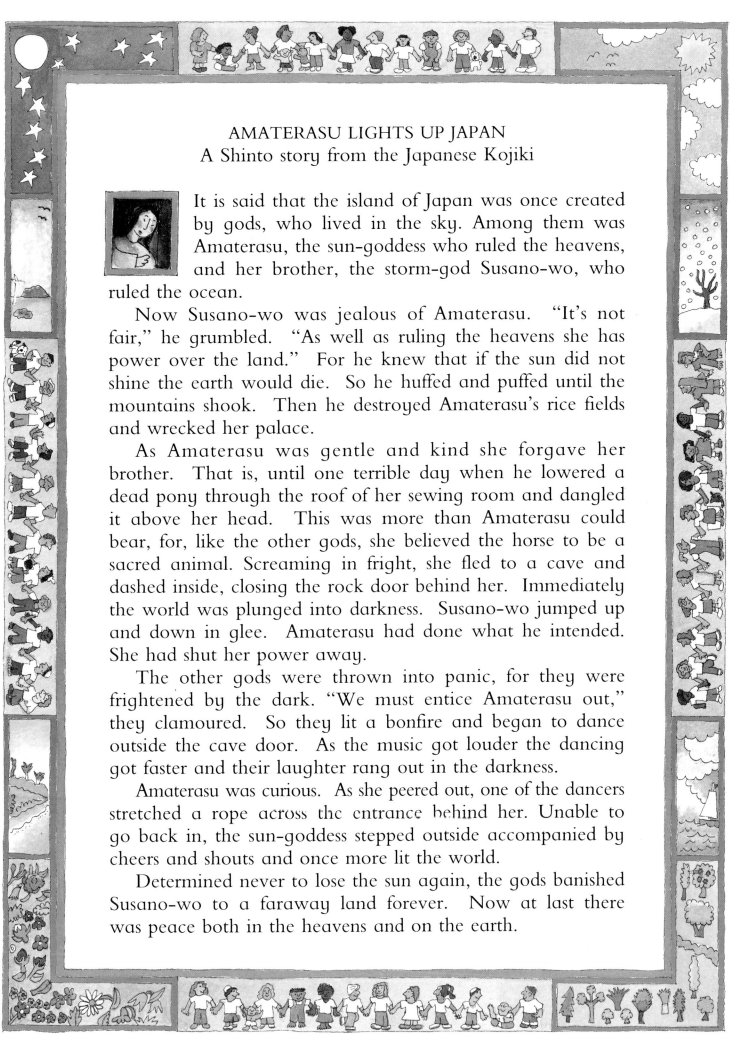

It is said that the island of Japan was once created by gods, who lived in the sky. Among them was Amaterasu, the sun-goddess who ruled the heavens, and her brother, the storm-god Susano-wo, who ruled the ocean.

Now Susano-wo was jealous of Amaterasu. "It's not fair," he grumbled. "As well as ruling the heavens she has power over the land." For he knew that if the sun did not shine the earth would die. So he huffed and puffed until the mountains shook. Then he destroyed Amaterasu's rice fields and wrecked her palace.

As Amaterasu was gentle and kind she forgave her brother. That is, until one terrible day when he lowered a dead pony through the roof of her sewing room and dangled it above her head. This was more than Amaterasu could bear, for, like the other gods, she believed the horse to be a sacred animal. Screaming in fright, she fled to a cave and dashed inside, closing the rock door behind her. Immediately the world was plunged into darkness. Susano-wo jumped up and down in glee. Amaterasu had done what he intended. She had shut her power away.

The other gods were thrown into panic, for they were frightened by the dark. "We must entice Amaterasu out," they clamoured. So they lit a bonfire and began to dance outside the cave door. As the music got louder the dancing got faster and their laughter rang out in the darkness.

Amaterasu was curious. As she peered out, one of the dancers stretched a rope across the entrance behind her. Unable to go back in, the sun-goddess stepped outside accompanied by cheers and shouts and once more lit the world.

Determined never to lose the sun again, the gods banished Susano-wo to a faraway land forever. Now at last there was peace both in the heavens and on the earth.

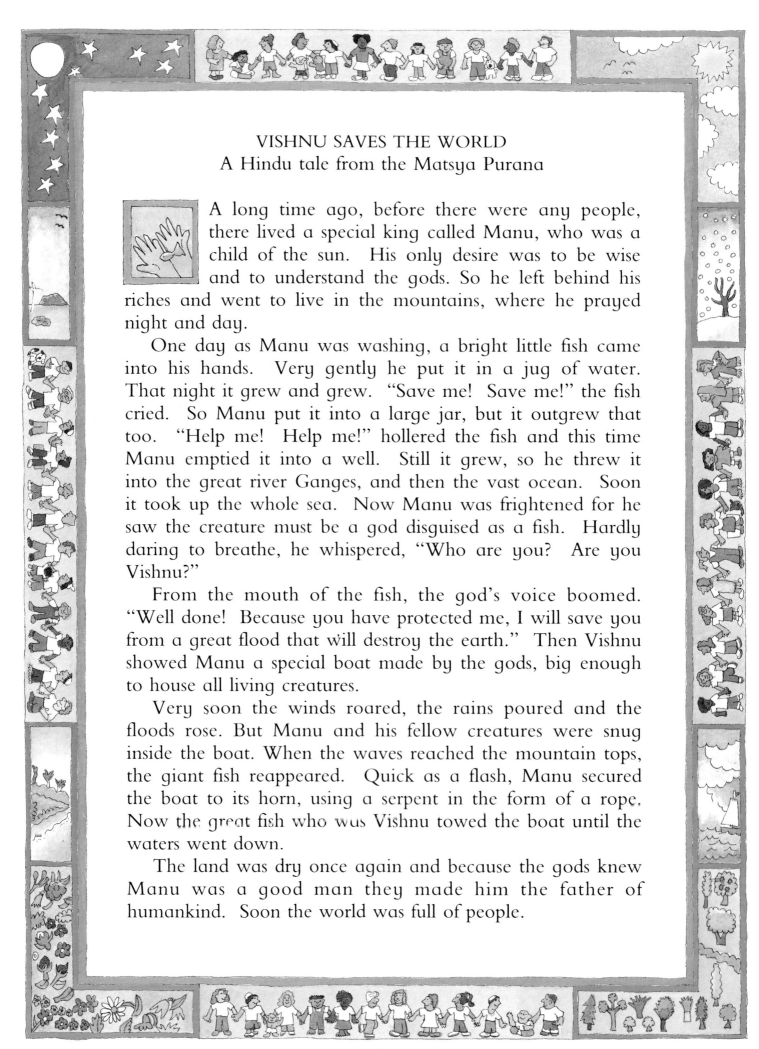

VISHNU SAVES THE WORLD
A Hindu tale from the Matsya Purana

A long time ago, before there were any people, there lived a special king called Manu, who was a child of the sun. His only desire was to be wise and to understand the gods. So he left behind his riches and went to live in the mountains, where he prayed night and day.

One day as Manu was washing, a bright little fish came into his hands. Very gently he put it in a jug of water. That night it grew and grew. "Save me! Save me!" the fish cried. So Manu put it into a large jar, but it outgrew that too. "Help me! Help me!" hollered the fish and this time Manu emptied it into a well. Still it grew, so he threw it into the great river Ganges, and then the vast ocean. Soon it took up the whole sea. Now Manu was frightened for he saw the creature must be a god disguised as a fish. Hardly daring to breathe, he whispered, "Who are you? Are you Vishnu?"

From the mouth of the fish, the god's voice boomed. "Well done! Because you have protected me, I will save you from a great flood that will destroy the earth." Then Vishnu showed Manu a special boat made by the gods, big enough to house all living creatures.

Very soon the winds roared, the rains poured and the floods rose. But Manu and his fellow creatures were snug inside the boat. When the waves reached the mountain tops, the giant fish reappeared. Quick as a flash, Manu secured the boat to its horn, using a serpent in the form of a rope. Now the great fish who was Vishnu towed the boat until the waters went down.

The land was dry once again and because the gods knew Manu was a good man they made him the father of humankind. Soon the world was full of people.

28

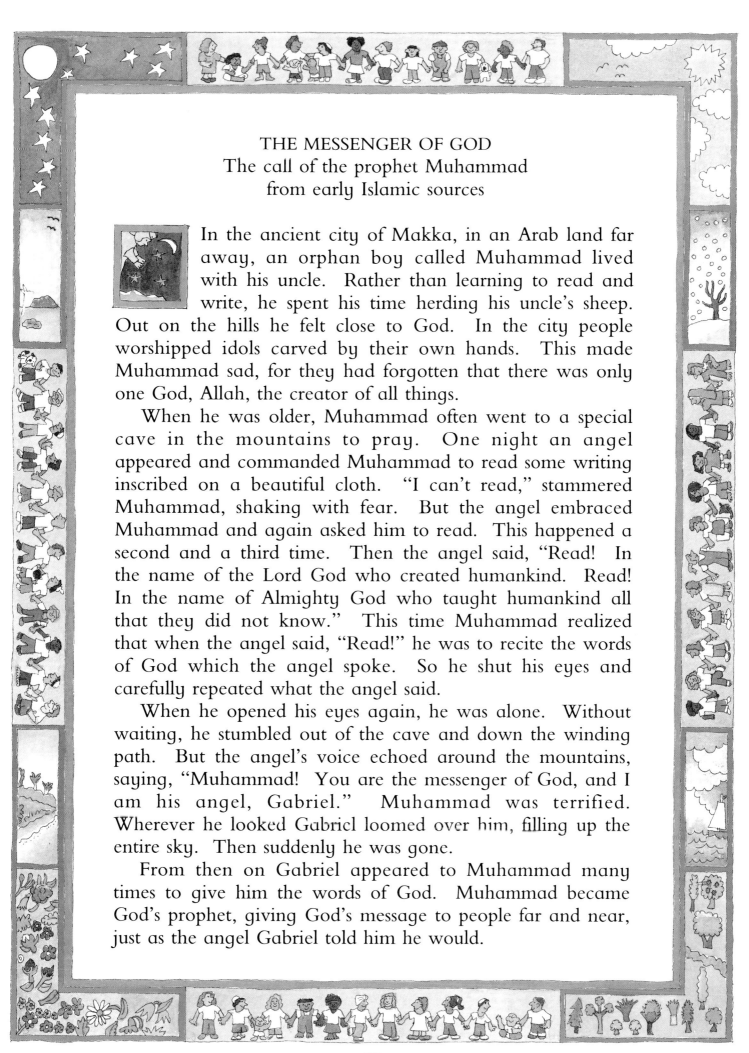

THE MESSENGER OF GOD
The call of the prophet Muhammad
from early Islamic sources

In the ancient city of Makka, in an Arab land far away, an orphan boy called Muhammad lived with his uncle. Rather than learning to read and write, he spent his time herding his uncle's sheep. Out on the hills he felt close to God. In the city people worshipped idols carved by their own hands. This made Muhammad sad, for they had forgotten that there was only one God, Allah, the creator of all things.

When he was older, Muhammad often went to a special cave in the mountains to pray. One night an angel appeared and commanded Muhammad to read some writing inscribed on a beautiful cloth. "I can't read," stammered Muhammad, shaking with fear. But the angel embraced Muhammad and again asked him to read. This happened a second and a third time. Then the angel said, "Read! In the name of the Lord God who created humankind. Read! In the name of Almighty God who taught humankind all that they did not know." This time Muhammad realized that when the angel said, "Read!" he was to recite the words of God which the angel spoke. So he shut his eyes and carefully repeated what the angel said.

When he opened his eyes again, he was alone. Without waiting, he stumbled out of the cave and down the winding path. But the angel's voice echoed around the mountains, saying, "Muhammad! You are the messenger of God, and I am his angel, Gabriel." Muhammad was terrified. Wherever he looked Gabriel loomed over him, filling up the entire sky. Then suddenly he was gone.

From then on Gabriel appeared to Muhammad many times to give him the words of God. Muhammad became God's prophet, giving God's message to people far and near, just as the angel Gabriel told him he would.

THE BURNING BUSH
A story from Exodus, the second book of the Jewish Torah

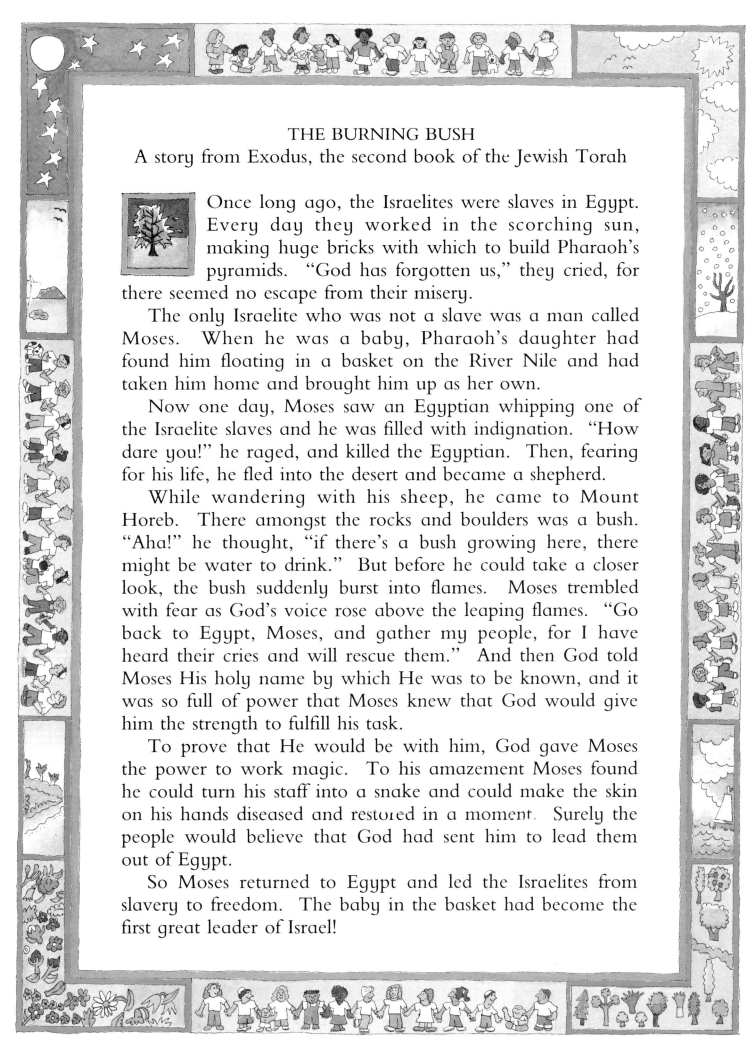

Once long ago, the Israelites were slaves in Egypt. Every day they worked in the scorching sun, making huge bricks with which to build Pharaoh's pyramids. "God has forgotten us," they cried, for there seemed no escape from their misery.

The only Israelite who was not a slave was a man called Moses. When he was a baby, Pharaoh's daughter had found him floating in a basket on the River Nile and had taken him home and brought him up as her own.

Now one day, Moses saw an Egyptian whipping one of the Israelite slaves and he was filled with indignation. "How dare you!" he raged, and killed the Egyptian. Then, fearing for his life, he fled into the desert and became a shepherd.

While wandering with his sheep, he came to Mount Horeb. There amongst the rocks and boulders was a bush. "Aha!" he thought, "if there's a bush growing here, there might be water to drink." But before he could take a closer look, the bush suddenly burst into flames. Moses trembled with fear as God's voice rose above the leaping flames. "Go back to Egypt, Moses, and gather my people, for I have heard their cries and will rescue them." And then God told Moses His holy name by which He was to be known, and it was so full of power that Moses knew that God would give him the strength to fulfill his task.

To prove that He would be with him, God gave Moses the power to work magic. To his amazement Moses found he could turn his staff into a snake and could make the skin on his hands diseased and restored in a moment. Surely the people would believe that God had sent him to lead them out of Egypt.

So Moses returned to Egypt and led the Israelites from slavery to freedom. The baby in the basket had become the first great leader of Israel!

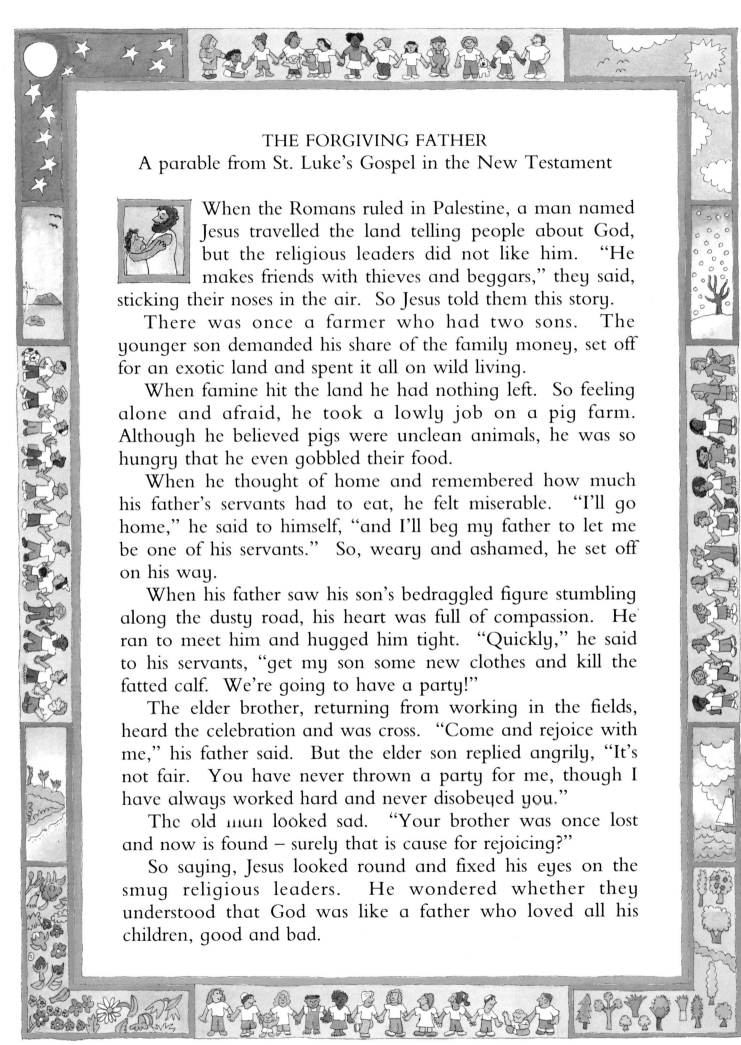

THE FORGIVING FATHER
A parable from St. Luke's Gospel in the New Testament

When the Romans ruled in Palestine, a man named Jesus travelled the land telling people about God, but the religious leaders did not like him. "He makes friends with thieves and beggars," they said, sticking their noses in the air. So Jesus told them this story.

There was once a farmer who had two sons. The younger son demanded his share of the family money, set off for an exotic land and spent it all on wild living.

When famine hit the land he had nothing left. So feeling alone and afraid, he took a lowly job on a pig farm. Although he believed pigs were unclean animals, he was so hungry that he even gobbled their food.

When he thought of home and remembered how much his father's servants had to eat, he felt miserable. "I'll go home," he said to himself, "and I'll beg my father to let me be one of his servants." So, weary and ashamed, he set off on his way.

When his father saw his son's bedraggled figure stumbling along the dusty road, his heart was full of compassion. He ran to meet him and hugged him tight. "Quickly," he said to his servants, "get my son some new clothes and kill the fatted calf. We're going to have a party!"

The elder brother, returning from working in the fields, heard the celebration and was cross. "Come and rejoice with me," his father said. But the elder son replied angrily, "It's not fair. You have never thrown a party for me, though I have always worked hard and never disobeyed you."

The old man looked sad. "Your brother was once lost and now is found – surely that is cause for rejoicing?"

So saying, Jesus looked round and fixed his eyes on the smug religious leaders. He wondered whether they understood that God was like a father who loved all his children, good and bad.

34

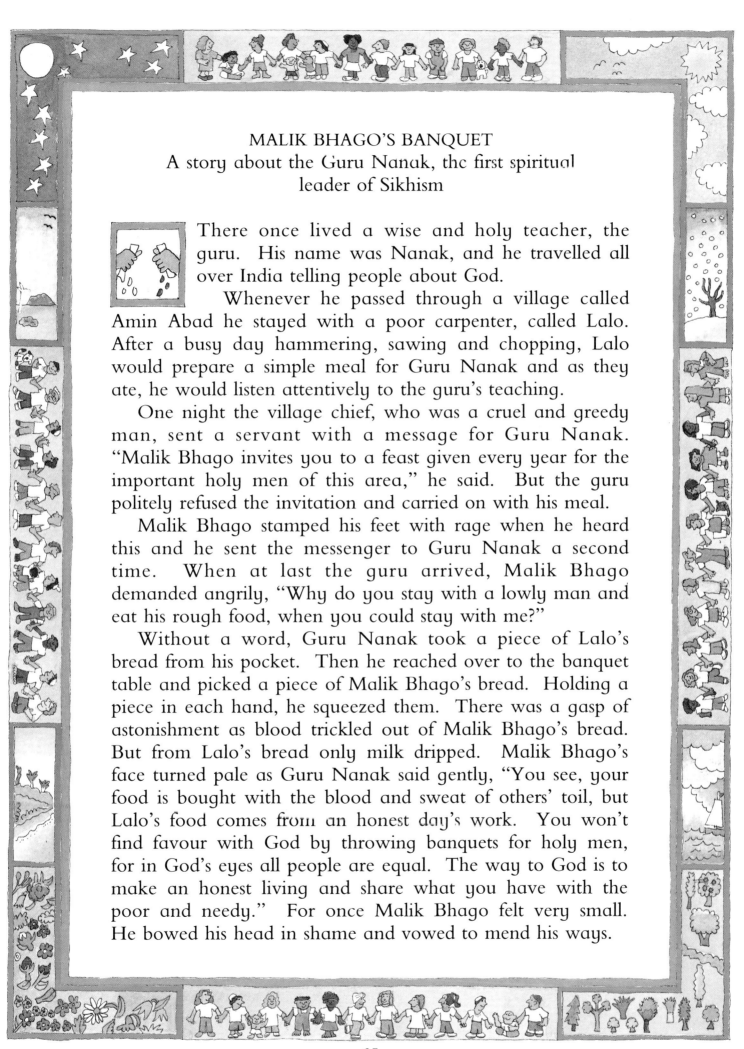

MALIK BHAGO'S BANQUET
A story about the Guru Nanak, the first spiritual leader of Sikhism

There once lived a wise and holy teacher, the guru. His name was Nanak, and he travelled all over India telling people about God.

Whenever he passed through a village called Amin Abad he stayed with a poor carpenter, called Lalo. After a busy day hammering, sawing and chopping, Lalo would prepare a simple meal for Guru Nanak and as they ate, he would listen attentively to the guru's teaching.

One night the village chief, who was a cruel and greedy man, sent a servant with a message for Guru Nanak. "Malik Bhago invites you to a feast given every year for the important holy men of this area," he said. But the guru politely refused the invitation and carried on with his meal.

Malik Bhago stamped his feet with rage when he heard this and he sent the messenger to Guru Nanak a second time. When at last the guru arrived, Malik Bhago demanded angrily, "Why do you stay with a lowly man and eat his rough food, when you could stay with me?"

Without a word, Guru Nanak took a piece of Lalo's bread from his pocket. Then he reached over to the banquet table and picked a piece of Malik Bhago's bread. Holding a piece in each hand, he squeezed them. There was a gasp of astonishment as blood trickled out of Malik Bhago's bread. But from Lalo's bread only milk dripped. Malik Bhago's face turned pale as Guru Nanak said gently, "You see, your food is bought with the blood and sweat of others' toil, but Lalo's food comes from an honest day's work. You won't find favour with God by throwing banquets for holy men, for in God's eyes all people are equal. The way to God is to make an honest living and share what you have with the poor and needy." For once Malik Bhago felt very small. He bowed his head in shame and vowed to mend his ways.

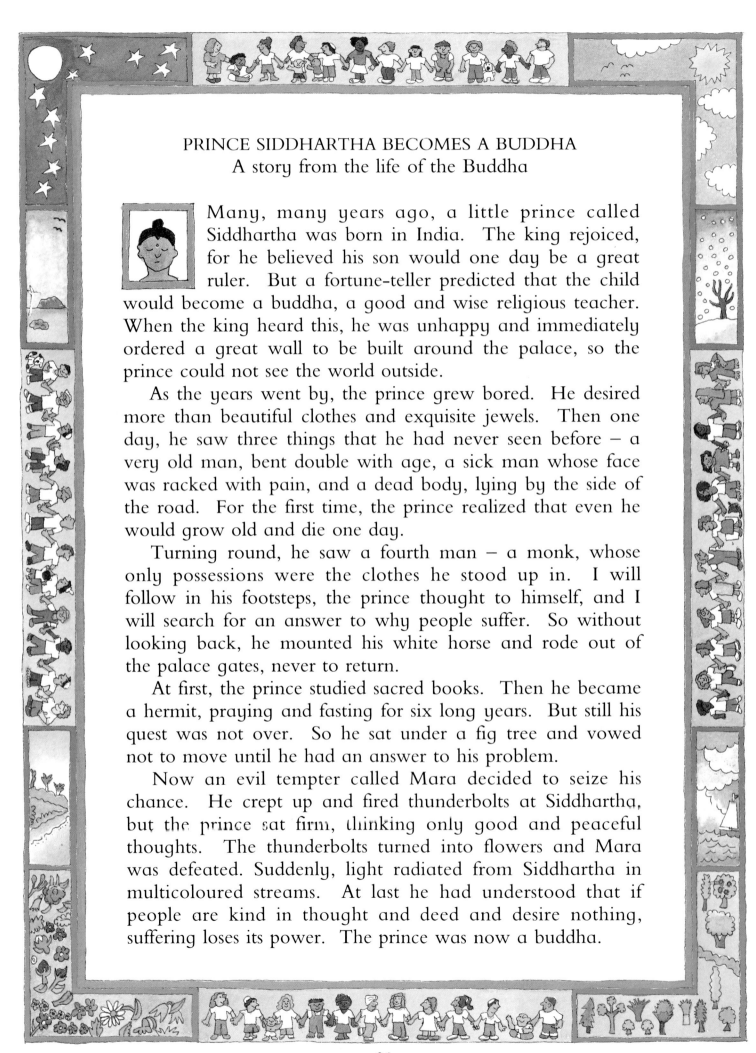

PRINCE SIDDHARTHA BECOMES A BUDDHA
A story from the life of the Buddha

Many, many years ago, a little prince called Siddhartha was born in India. The king rejoiced, for he believed his son would one day be a great ruler. But a fortune-teller predicted that the child would become a buddha, a good and wise religious teacher. When the king heard this, he was unhappy and immediately ordered a great wall to be built around the palace, so the prince could not see the world outside.

As the years went by, the prince grew bored. He desired more than beautiful clothes and exquisite jewels. Then one day, he saw three things that he had never seen before – a very old man, bent double with age, a sick man whose face was racked with pain, and a dead body, lying by the side of the road. For the first time, the prince realized that even he would grow old and die one day.

Turning round, he saw a fourth man – a monk, whose only possessions were the clothes he stood up in. I will follow in his footsteps, the prince thought to himself, and I will search for an answer to why people suffer. So without looking back, he mounted his white horse and rode out of the palace gates, never to return.

At first, the prince studied sacred books. Then he became a hermit, praying and fasting for six long years. But still his quest was not over. So he sat under a fig tree and vowed not to move until he had an answer to his problem.

Now an evil tempter called Mara decided to seize his chance. He crept up and fired thunderbolts at Siddhartha, but the prince sat firm, thinking only good and peaceful thoughts. The thunderbolts turned into flowers and Mara was defeated. Suddenly, light radiated from Siddhartha in multicoloured streams. At last he had understood that if people are kind in thought and deed and desire nothing, suffering loses its power. The prince was now a buddha.

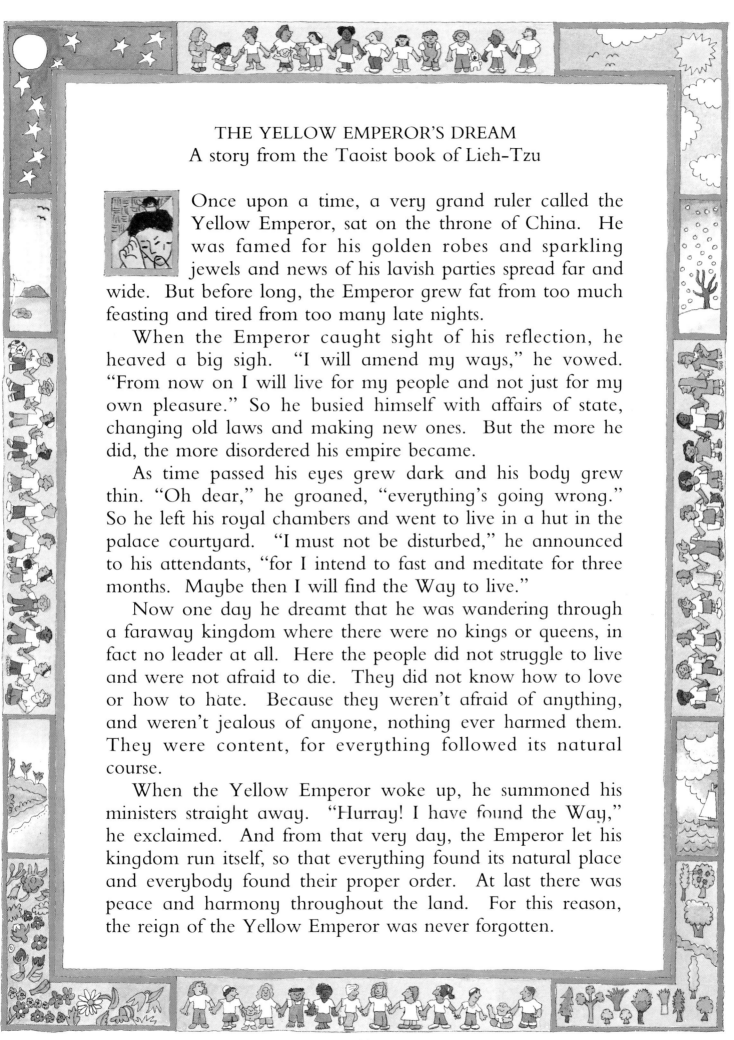

THE YELLOW EMPEROR'S DREAM
A story from the Taoist book of Lieh-Tzu

Once upon a time, a very grand ruler called the Yellow Emperor, sat on the throne of China. He was famed for his golden robes and sparkling jewels and news of his lavish parties spread far and wide. But before long, the Emperor grew fat from too much feasting and tired from too many late nights.

When the Emperor caught sight of his reflection, he heaved a big sigh. "I will amend my ways," he vowed. "From now on I will live for my people and not just for my own pleasure." So he busied himself with affairs of state, changing old laws and making new ones. But the more he did, the more disordered his empire became.

As time passed his eyes grew dark and his body grew thin. "Oh dear," he groaned, "everything's going wrong." So he left his royal chambers and went to live in a hut in the palace courtyard. "I must not be disturbed," he announced to his attendants, "for I intend to fast and meditate for three months. Maybe then I will find the Way to live."

Now one day he dreamt that he was wandering through a faraway kingdom where there were no kings or queens, in fact no leader at all. Here the people did not struggle to live and were not afraid to die. They did not know how to love or how to hate. Because they weren't afraid of anything, and weren't jealous of anyone, nothing ever harmed them. They were content, for everything followed its natural course.

When the Yellow Emperor woke up, he summoned his ministers straight away. "Hurray! I have found the Way," he exclaimed. And from that very day, the Emperor let his kingdom run itself, so that everything found its natural place and everybody found their proper order. At last there was peace and harmony throughout the land. For this reason, the reign of the Yellow Emperor was never forgotten.